THE HISTORY OF
FIRE ENGINES

THE HISTORY OF
FIRE ENGINES

BY JOHN A. CALDERONE

BARNES
&NOBLE
BOOKS
NEW YORK

This edition published by
Barnes & Noble, Inc.,
by arrangement with Brompton Books
Corporation.

Produced by Brompton Books
Corporation
15 Sherwood Place
Greenwich, CT 06830

ISBN 0-7607-0101-6

Printed in China

Design by Elena Miranda

*Page 1: This colorful American
LaFrance pumper protected Middletown,
NY, and was a popular attraction at area
musters.*

*Page 2: Development of hose capable of
being packed flat led to the introduction
of hose wagons. This restored unit, an
1898 American, served Lawrence, MA.*

*Above: Typical of the classic fire appara-
tus produced during the 1950s, this 1954
Ward LaFrance 750 gpm pumper has an
open cab, limited compartmentation, and
all equipment is carried exposed, ready
for rapid use. This unit originally served
New York City and is shown in service at
the U.S. Coast Guard Base Fire
Department on Governor's Island, NY.*

To Eddie, John & Mariel

CONTENTS

INTRODUCTION

Fire is one of man's greatest discoveries. It was shortly after this discovery, or perhaps even simultaneously, however, that man realized the need to suppress fire. From that moment on, man has sought the most effective means to fight the destruction and ravages of fire.

The development of firefighting apparatus parallels the advancement of technology from the beginning of organized society. Ancient civilizations as early as 200 B.C. were protected from fire by crude mechanical pumps. History shows that these pumps evolved through the ages into today's modern fire engine.

While developments in firefighting apparatus reflected advancements in technology, the fire engine was also greatly influenced by war, sociological changes, experimentation, environmental issues, ever-changing standards and regulations, and by a very proud tradition. Technology and change have made the fire engine the impressive, efficient and functional vehicle it is today, but it is the pride and tradition that fascinates us.

For many of us, the shiny, red fire engine evokes pleasant childhood memories of trips to the firehouse, of parades, and of running alongside the truck as it passed us by. Indeed, the fire engine is a part of American history itself. In small towns all across America, communities ran fund raisers to purchase, maintain or restore their fire engine, a practice that continues today. Those of us from large cities always seem able to remember how old we were when the firehouse on our block received a new fire engine. We may not know its year, make or model, but somehow we all seem to associate one particular fire engine with our youthful years.

Our fascination with the fire engine is something that transcends time and age. It is so easy to share a child's excitement at seeing the fire trucks roar down the street. Few can resist the opportunity to recall memories of open cab trucks, shiny chrome bells, hand cranked sirens, and of firefighters riding on the outside of the trucks. Yet, it is the fire engines of today that will provide tomorrow's memories. Fortunately, we never outgrow our enthusiasm for and fascination with the fire engine, nor should we.

BEFORE MOTORS

The earliest form of organized fire protection in North America was the citizen bucket brigade. Eventually a big step forward occurred when hand pumpers that were pulled to the scene by firefighters were developed. Hand pumpers, sometimes called hand tubs, had long parallel handles that required many volunteers to pump up and down rapidly, pumping water from its "tub." While the effectiveness of hand pumpers was limited by the volunteers' capacity to pump before becoming exhausted, these pumpers far exceeded the capabilities of the bucket brigade. Hand pumpers built in England by Newsham and shipped by boat to Neu Amsterdam (New York) during the early 1700s were the first fire apparatus to serve in the United States. American manufacturers copied and refined these machines for almost 100 years.

A revolution in firefighting technology occurred with the development of the steam pumper in England in the early 1800s. Steam was created by firing the boiler with coal and the power created was transferred to enable the unit to supply water to hoses. Most steamers had piston pumps while some had rotary gear pumps. A practical steam pumper was built and

Above: This wooden hand tub, built around 1725, was among the earliest firefighting equipment to protect early America.

Left: The goose-neck style hand pumper saw service in the early part of the nineteenth century. It was characterized by its long arms that many firefighters would use to pump.

demonstrated in New York around 1840, but volunteer firefighters, perceiving the apparatus as a threat to their existence, took a strong stand against it. The steam pumper could more effectively supply continuous water without wearing out the great amount of manpower that was required to operate hand pumpers, thereby depleting the ranks of volunteers required.

The widespread introduction of steam pumpers and the death knell of the volunteers in major American cities was signaled by the establishment of the first paid firefighting force in the United States, in Cincinnati in 1853. This was also the beginning of what is considered the most colorful era in firefighting, distinguished by new concepts, inventions, technological advances, heroism, and establishment of traditions.

Early American firefighting apparatus were pulled to the scene by volunteer firefighters. This required a large number of men, especially in hilly areas and when there was snow on the ground. Once the apparatus reached the scene, the exhausted firefighters still had to fight the fire. In some areas, hand-drawn apparatus existed as late as the 1860s.

There had to be a better way, and in many cities this came by the replacement of the volunteers with paid firefighters. Cities could not afford to pay the large number of firefighters required to pull apparatus to fires; consequently, horses were utilized for this purpose. Hand-drawn apparatus were quickly replaced by the more efficient horse-drawn apparatus. Lighter apparatus were capable of being pulled by one

Top left: A double deck style hand pumper that served around the middle of the nineteenth century, at the time that steam pumpers were being introduced.

Left: Warren Engine Company 1, of Roxbury, MA, turns out of quarters pulling their hand pumper, around 1868.

Left: A typical early ladder truck, with no provisions for firefighters to ride on it.

Below: A horse-drawn steamer responds in New York City. Three horse hitches were common on heavier apparatus, or where hills were normally encountered when responding.

or two horses. Those that were heavier or responded in hilly districts or in snow, used three or more horses.

While the job of pulling the apparatus was given over to the horses, early horse-drawn apparatus had limited riding positions for personnel. There had never been a need for anyone to ride on the apparatus because everyone helped pull it to the fire. Firefighters were still running to the fire with the horses pulling the apparatus and arriving in less than perfect condition to start firefighting operations.

In the late 1860s, "running boards" began to be installed on the sides of ladder trucks so that firefighters could ride the apparatus to the scene. It is interesting to note that the term "running boards" was used instead of "side step" or some other term, as the boards were used in place of running to the fire. This was a major innovation in apparatus design which exists on apparatus to this day, even though most contemporary apparatus have fully enclosed seating for the entire crew.

While providing riding positions on ladder trucks was relatively simple, doing the same for engine companies proved more difficult. Steamers provided two seated positions to accommodate the driver and usually the officer, with a small step at the rear of the boiler where a third firefighter could

Above: A heavier four-wheel hose reel from Bradlee Hose 10 in Boston, around 1878.

Right: A modified hose tender, rebuilt from a standard hose reel to provide riding positions allowing firefighters to ride to the fire.

stand. There was no practical way to add additional riding positions to steamers. The answer to this problem was to totally redesign the hose tender, which, at this time, was a two-wheel hose reel with seating available for only the driver. Existing hose tenders were retrofitted with four seats topside, above the hose reel, and a rear step was added. While this solved the riding situation, it resulted in another problem. The addition of a rear step eliminated the hose tender's fuel box. This led to the establishment of separate fuel wagons that provided sufficient fuel supply to keep the steamer operating at large fires. Some departments operated larger, four-wheel hose reels.

A wide variety of apparatus were developed during the horse-drawn era. Horse-drawn hose reels replaced the hand-drawn hose carriages. Development of hose capable of being packed flat led to the development of hose wagons, which were also equipped with deck pipes and carried other equipment and supplies, acting as a tender to the steamer. Most modern engine companies of this era responded with a steamer and hose wagon as a two-piece unit, with separate hose and engine companies being combined.

Hand-drawn ladder trucks, carrying portable ladders, hooks and other equipment were supplanted by larger, longer, horse-drawn units, leading to the development of the tiller position to steer the rear wheels, enabling these long units to maneuver in congested cities. The development of the wood aerial ladder, which extended up to 85 feet in height, took the ladder truck one step further.

To provide quick knockdown while steamers were being set up and hose lines stretched and also to extinguish smaller fires, the chemical unit was developed. These units carried tanks of bicarbonate of soda that, when activated by sulfuric acid, was expelled through small diameter, usually 3/4-inch, rubber hose on the fire. Most were one-horse, two-wheel units, although larger, four-wheel units were built. Separate chemical units were quite common in larger cities where they could respond faster than the larger steamers and hose tenders, and provide a quick attack, controlling most fires. Later, chemical equipment was installed on hose wagons, known as combination wagons, and operated as part of engine companies.

Originally, chief officers ran on foot to fires in their districts. In some departments, where the chief had an unusually large response area, a horse was provided for the chief. Eventually, a horse-drawn carriage, or chief's buggy, was developed.

The American fire service has always had its share of specialized units, and the horse-drawn era was no exception. Fuel tenders carried coal and wood to resupply steamers and

Left: A restored 1897 American Fire Engine Company steamer that formerly served Cedarhurst, NY.

Right: Running boards added to the sides of ladder trucks allowed ladder company firefighters to ride to the fire. Here, New York City's Hook & Ladder 30 responds in Harlem.

keep them in operation at large fires. The water tower, a portable tower mast, was capable of applying water to upper floors of a burning building. Trained horses were a fire department's most valuable asset and larger departments operated horse-drawn ambulances for sick and injured horses, even before this service was provided to firefighters. Turret wagons and fireboat tenders carried larger diameter hose and were equipped with large deck pipes to supply large volumes of water at major fires. Steam powered searchlight units provided fireground lighting. Many other unusual and unique specialized units were developed to fill local requirements.

In 1867, Amoskeag, a builder of steam pumpers, constructed a self-propelled steam pumper. Its motive power was supplied by sprocket chains connecting a shaft on the pump to the rear wheels. The driver steered and controlled the brakes while the engineer, standing on the rear step, controlled the speed, leading to many confusing situations. The speed control was a locomotive-type throttle. On a fair road, the apparatus was capable of 10 mph. A major problem with this type of unit was its erratic behavior while rounding corners since both driving wheels always turned at the same speed. Although a

Above: Prior to being assigned buggies, chief officers would run to fires in their districts on foot. If they were assigned to very large response areas, they sometimes had horses.

Right: Two and four-wheel chemical units provided rapid attack and attempted to prevent further fire spread while hose wagons stretched hose lines from steamers.

Right: Even before firefighters were provided this service, ambulances were available for fire horses. Training a good fire horse was more expensive than training firefighters at the time.

Below: A restored 1886 Hayes aerial ladder that protected Lynchburg, VA. Note the tiller seat positioned beneath the aerial ladder at the rear.

Right: Among the more unusual horse-drawn special units were several steam-powered searchlight engines operated by New York City. These steamers did not supply water, only power to light the fire scene.

Page 15: Amoskeag developed these unusual self-propelled steamers, using the steam to generate propulsion for the vehicle. They were slow, heavy, and difficult to operate, but were an interesting experiment before the development of the gasoline engine. This 1897 model saw service as Engine 35 in Boston.

Below: Ornate lanterns, often with decorative glass that identified the individual fire company, were common on early hand and horse-drawn fire apparatus.

good number of these innovative units were sold, they were heavier and much slower than horse-drawn steamers and many were eventually converted to horse-drawn units.

The first successful wood aerial ladder was patented by Daniel Hayes in 1868. The tillerman on these early aerials sat beneath the aerial ladder, not on top as later became common. The rights to this patent were eventually sold to LaFrance. Other early aerial ladder manufacturers included the Fire Extinguisher Manufacturing Company, Babcock, and Dederick. Originally requiring several firefighters to raise it by hand through a series of gears and pulleys, several manufacturers developed spring-assisted raising mechanisms in the early 1900s.

The first water tower to enter service was fabricated by John Hogan and Abner Greenleaf in 1879. It consisted of a 50-foot mast of pipe sections which had to be assembled to attain the desired height, then raised manually by cranks and gears which engaged a trunion to which the tower pipe was attached. It was pulled by two horses. The design, tower height, raising mechanisms, and equipment carried by water towers evolved over the years into an efficient, vital apparatus.

The invention of cotton-jacketed hose, replacing rubber hose, allowed for hose to be carried flat instead of on reels. In the late 1880s, hose wagons, with hose loads packed flat in the wagon beds, started to replace the hose reels. Hose wagons also provided better riding positions and more space to carry tools, fittings, and nozzles, which had been severely limited on the older hose tenders.

Many of the early hand-drawn apparatus were lavishly decorated with striping, paintings, and logos. This tradition was carried over onto the horse-drawn units and evolved into ornate gold leafing, outlined stripes to accent color schemes, unit numbers and department names. Steamers were especially attractive

with lots of polished chrome and other brightwork in addition to their lavish paintwork. The colors of horse-drawn apparatus varied as much as modern apparatus do today. Colors such as dark green, brown, maroon, white, red and combinations of these were popular, depending on local desires.

Major apparatus builders during the horse-drawn era included Ahrens, American, Amoskeag, Button, Clapp & Jones, Combination Ladder Company, International Fire Engine Company, LaFrance, Latta, Pirsch, Seagrave, Silsby, Waterous, and many others. There were also a great number of small, local firms producing fire apparatus during this era. Many of these firms continued producing fire apparatus into the motorized era. Others merged with or were taken over by other companies. Some ceased production of fire apparatus, never building motorized units.

Left: Boston's Engine 7 operated this hose wagon that was typical of those in use in major cities prior to motorization.

Right: The water tower was used to deliver large volumes of water to upper floors of burning structures. Many were motorized and saw service for many more years.

THE EARLY MOTORIZED ERA

Although some fire departments experimented with electric vehicles, the earliest motorized vehicles to serve in numbers were runabouts assigned to chief officers. However, just as steam power was seen as a threat, motorized fire apparatus was looked at as unreliable and unable to replace the much-loved horses. It took several decades for this changeover to take place nationwide, with steamers and other horse-drawn firefighting vehicles continuing in production.

Seagrave, a Columbus, Ohio, based apparatus manufacturer, introduced the first spring raising mechanism to hoist aerial ladders quickly from the bedded position in 1902. This job, previously done manually by several firefighters, suddenly became quicker, but it was still necessary to rotate and extend the aerial manually. American LaFrance followed with their own spring

assist mechanism two years later. Eventually, all aerial ladder manufacturers would produce such devices.

In 1903, the American LaFrance Fire Engine Company emerged from the consolidation of several other fire equipment manufacturers, and worked from a large plant located in Elmira, New York. One of the largest producers of American firefighting vehicles, despite mergers, corporate takeovers, and sales, American LaFrance survives to this date, producing custom fire apparatus chassis.

The size and weight of horse-drawn apparatus had grown so that most horses running at top speed would begin to slow down after about a half-mile. Many responses were longer than this distance. Studies done shortly after motor vehicles began to appear projected that a motorized fire company could be operated

The Mack Model AC, known as the "Bulldog" for its rugged appearance and performance, became a popular chassis for fire apparatus. This 1918 AC-model tractor was used to motorize a Baltimore City 1908 Hayes 85-foot aerial that was originally horse-drawn. The tillerman on this unit sat beneath the aerial ladder.

Above: A high pressure hose wagon and water tower operate large caliber streams into a loft building fire in New York City. The high pressure hose wagon was equipped with a large deck pipe and carried hose designed to withstand higher than normal pressures. The water tower was capable of placing a stream of water into the upper floors of burning buildings.

Above right: Reluctance to fully accept gasoline power led to a number of unusual hybrid apparatus being built. These units had gasoline powered pumps that were mounted on horse-drawn chassis. This pumper was built by Westinghouse and served in New York City.

at approximately one-third the cost of operating a horse-drawn unit of the same type, considering such factors as gasoline, oil, and maintenance versus feed, veterinary services, horse shoeing, stable equipment, and harnesses. The cost of using horses would continue to rise. Departments that still used horses in 1915 found that it was five times more expensive than motorized apparatus. The time had come for motorization.

Based on available historical records, 1906 is generally accepted as the beginning of the motorized age in the American fire service. During that year, a unique motorized pumper, built by Waterous, was placed into service at the Radnor Fire Company in Wayne, Pennsylvania. This pumper was unique because it was equipped with two gasoline motors, one for vehicle propulsion and the other to power the pump. Waterous has continued producing pumps and today is one of the leading suppliers of fire pumps. Also during this year, the Combination Ladder Company built a squad body, mounted on a Knox chassis, and delivered it to Springfield, Massachusetts. This vehicle was used to transport additional manpower to fires. Before the year was finished, Knox and the Combination Ladder Company were advertising a wide range of motorized fire apparatus that included hose wagons, chemical wagons, squad units and chief's cars.

Left: The first custom-built American LaFrance fire apparatus was constructed in 1910. Registration #1 was a combination chemical hose wagon and served Lenox, MA. It has been restored and is a popular feature at New England antique fire apparatus musters.

Below: Some lanterns on early fire apparatus, in addition to serving as identification of the individual unit, actually provided some light, as modern apparatus lights do.

A small number of unusual hybrid fire apparatus appeared in the early part of the century. Howe, Waterous, and Westinghouse all built gasoline powered pumpers that were mounted on horse-drawn chassis. These units had pumps that were powered by a gasoline engine, but were still pulled to the scene by horses. This design was somewhat pointless considering that the gasoline engine could have also driven the vehicle. Only a handful of this type were constructed.

After several years of development, in 1907 Seagrave completed its first motorized firefighting vehicle, a combination chemical hose wagon. Later in the year, the first production model Seagrave motorized apparatus were delivered to Vancouver, British Columbia. American LaFrance also built its first motorized unit that year, a chemical wagon on a Simplex chassis, probably built as a demonstrator unit. It would be a few more years before American LaFrance began regular deliveries of motorized units. Several other manufacturers entered the field around this time, including Webb and Howe. Many of the early motorized apparatus were built on touring car and similar chassis and most had chain-drive and wood-spoked, solid rubber tires. Few had windshields. White was an extremely popular color for early motorized fire apparatus, as were the darker shades of red.

The Ahrens-Fox Fire Engine Company was formed in Cincinnati, Ohio, during 1908. Most noted for its piston pumpers with the pump and chrome ball chamber out front, ahead of the engine, Ahrens-Fox produced a variety of apparatus. The piston pump is a positive displacement pump with reciprocating pistons operating to force water from the pump chamber. New manufacturers, Autocar, Locomobile and Robinson among them, continued to enter the field as the demand for motorized fire apparatus increased. After building such units since 1867, Amoskeag produced its last self-propelled steamer in 1908, an indication that motorization was taking hold.

Up until this time, most engine companies had been operating with two apparatus: a steamer, that may have been tractor-

Ahrens-Fox broke from other fire apparatus manufacturers in introducing a non-conventional pumper design utilizing a front-mounted piston pump. This unit, owned by a restoration group in Branford, CT, is a 1919 model M-K-4, registration #858, that originally served Mt. Vernon, NY.

ized, and a hose wagon or combination chemical hose wagon. In 1909, a giant step forward was taken in fire apparatus development with the delivery of the first triple combination pumper. This vehicle provided three functions: it carried a pump, had a hose bed, and incorporated chemical tanks, in effect a pumper, hose wagon and chemical wagon all in one. This unique vehicle was built by Tea Tray Company, a small New Jersey fire apparatus builder, on an American Mors chassis and delivered to Middletown, New York. As developments in apparatus pro-

gressed, the chemical equipment on triple combination pumpers would be replaced by booster tanks and hose reels. However, this innovative delivery would eventually, albeit very slowly, change the manner in which most fire departments operated, replacing most two-piece pumper and hose wagon engine companies with one triple combination pumper and also eliminating the separate chemical companies.

Another major development in apparatus design occurred in 1909 when the International Motor Company, the forerunner

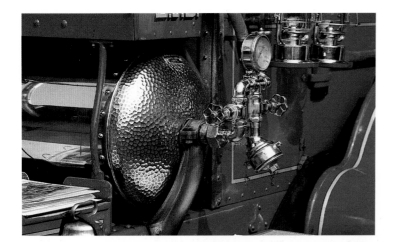

of Mack Trucks, sold a motorized tractor to Allentown, Pennsylvania, to motorize a former horse-drawn ladder truck. This is believed to be the first motorized ladder in the United States. Seagrave, a firm that would become a leader in aerial ladder manufacturing, delivered its first motorized aerial ladder truck during this year as well.

Many new ideas were being tried during the early motorized era. The Couple Gear Freight Wheel Company, in 1910, introduced electric motors mounted inside each wheel hub, supplied by battery power. This, in effect, provided four-wheel-drive capability, but apparatus that were notoriously slow and often ran out of battery power before completing their assignments. Despite these drawbacks, many such apparatus were sold,

Left: Before booster tanks, chemical tanks were mounted on various apparatus to provide for a rapid attack of the fire.
Below: The Christie Front Drive Auto Company produced approximately 600 of these tractors that were used to motorize all types of horse-drawn fire apparatus. This 1911 Christie was used to power an 1899 American steamer for the Community Fire Company in Wayne, NJ. Many other manufacturers also produced tractors to motorize horse-drawn fire apparatus.

Right: The nation's first rescue company, the forerunner of today's heavy rescues and urban search and rescue units, was organized in New York City during 1915. A modified Cadillac touring car chassis was used to carry the unit's specialized equipment.

Below: Ahrens-Fox marketed a piston pump that was mounted ahead of the engine on its pumpers. It was characterized by the large chrome ball.

including many tractors used to power former horse-drawn units. This was a cheaper alternative for fire departments wanting to replace horses rapidly. Several other manufacturers dabbled in electric powered fire apparatus, but the limitations of storage batteries and the availability of recharging facilities greatly handicapped their efficiency.

The first completely American LaFrance-built motorized fire apparatus, a combination chemical hose wagon, was delivered to Lenox, Massachusetts, during 1910, beginning a long line of custom-built units from this manufacturer.

Ahrens-Fox introduced a motorized pumper utilizing an unusual design during 1911. Instead of the conventional design of the time with the engine forward and the pump either under or to the rear of the driver's seat, Ahrens-Fox located its piston pump at the very front of the vehicle, ahead of the motor. This made for an unusually long length in front of the driver. While

these vehicles were real workhorses and well-liked by firefighters, they posed a problem in congested city driving; almost half the apparatus had to be stuck out into the intersection before the driver had a clear view of opposing traffic. The same year, Seagrave introduced its first motorized pumper, a centrifugal model, and both American LaFrance and Mack introduced pumpers equipped with rotary gear pumps. Centrifugal pumps use impellers to expel water by centrifugal force, while rotary gear pumps are positive displacement pumps with closely fitting gears that force water through the pump chamber.

The first of approximately 600 two-wheel tractors built by the Christie Front Drive Auto Company began to appear in 1912. These practical units went a long way towards motorizing large fleets of horse-drawn apparatus in cities throughout America and provided a stop-gap alternative until purpose-built motorized apparatus could be purchased. They were placed under steamers, ladder trucks and water towers, allowing departments to keep these apparatus in service. Other manufacturers followed suit with tractors of their own design. The market for these tractors lasted about ten years and produced some very interesting-looking conversions. Some fire departments, still not totally trusting gasoline engines, purchased hybrids: steamers mounted on gasoline powered chassis. These dinosaurs were outdated the day they were delivered but stubbornness and tradition prevailed. Other fire departments with limited funds or talented members created their own motorized fire apparatus utilizing the bodies from horse-drawn units or constructing makeshift bodywork and mounting them on whatever motorized chassis were available to them.

Ahrens-Fox introduced the booster car during 1913. This was a small apparatus equipped with a light duty pump, a water tank, and hose, which quickly replaced chemical units. This equipment was eventually incorporated onto pumpers as standard equipment, and occasionally is included on aerial ladders, rescue trucks, and other apparatus. A hand cranked siren was introduced that year to supplement the standard bell that had been the only audible warning device on fire apparatus up to this time.

Maxim, another firm whose name became well known in American fire apparatus history, began production of motorized fire apparatus during 1914, with the production of a hose wagon. This was followed in 1915 by a rotary gear pumper.

Production of the Model AC Mack "Bulldog" began in 1915. This chassis would become quite popular for fire apparatus with pumpers, hose wagons, rescue trucks, service ladder trucks, and tractors for aerials and water towers, all being built on it. It had a sturdy, rugged appearance, and performed in the same manner.

The nation's first unit organized specifically to handle unusual rescue situations was established in New York City in

Above: For many years, even into the 1960s in some fire departments, hand lanterns were carried on the sides of fire apparatus. Like their use in railroading, they were used to relay signals and as danger markers.

Left: Buffalo Fire Apparatus began producing firefighting vehicles in 1920. The Pioneer Hose Company in Robesonia, PA, operated this 1931 Buffalo 1000 gpm pumper.

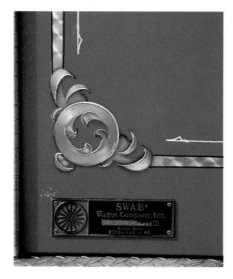

Above: Ornate gold-leaf scroll work was common on fire apparatus and contributes greatly to a fire truck's appearance.

1915. Equipped with "oxygen helmets," life lines, pulmotors, line shooting guns, hand tools, cutting torches and related equipment, their purpose was to operate at extremely smoky fires such as in subways, cellars and sub-cellars, perform difficult ventilation, stop ammonia leaks, and rescue collapse victims and trapped firefighters. The firefighters in this unit were recruited because of their qualifications in other fields; iron workers, electricians, construction workers, and other specialties. The rescue apparatus was a specially modified Cadillac chassis. This unit was the forerunner of the heavy rescue and urban search and rescue units in service throughout the United States today.

An air operated aerial ladder hoisting mechanism utilizing a compressor to raise the aerial out of its bed, was introduced by Dahill in 1916. The first motorized pumper produced by Pirsch entered service this year as well.

The Stutz Fire Engine Company, operating from Indianapolis, began production of fire apparatus in 1919 with the introduction of a pumper. Stutz would be a major apparatus builder into the next decade.

Another major fire apparatus manufacturer, Buffalo, began producing apparatus during 1920. This firm, operating from Buffalo, New York, produced a wide variety of apparatus into the 1940s.

By the early 1920s, most fire horses had disappeared from the scene, ending a colorful era in fire service history. By this time, the majority of fire apparatus in service was motorized, and pneumatic tires were beginning to appear on fire apparatus. Some major cities held retirement ceremonies marking the end of this era, with "last runs" staged and photographed. Some horse-drawn equipment remained as spare or reserve units, but were rarely used. Motorization had proven itself to be more cost effective than horses. The motor vehicle had developed to the point where it was relatively reliable, and faster than the horses. There were also other advantages that were rarely publicized. Since the horses were usually housed on the apparatus floor, adjacent to the apparatus for fast response, there always existed the need to maintain a clean, healthy environment for both horses and firefighters. This was a continuing daily battle that was never really won. When the horses left, so did many health hazards associated with them. Firefighters no longer lived in barns.

A new type of fire apparatus appeared during the early 1920s, the quad. Many departments operated city service trucks, units that carried portable ladders and other equipment normally carried by ladder companies, but without an aerial ladder. The quad combined the functions of the triple combination pumper

Right: This 55-foot water tower, built by the Fire Extinguisher Manufacturing Company in 1896, was originally horse-drawn. Typical of many horse-drawn apparatus built just before motorization, this unit was motorized with the addition of a 1917 Ahrens-Fox tractor. It served in Cincinnati and has been restored.

The quad is a single apparatus that provides the functions of four distinct apparatus: pumper, hose wagon, booster unit, and city service truck. Brookfield, NH, operated this Mack quad. The chain drive is clearly visible at the rear wheels.

with the added equipment of the city service truck into one vehicle. These units were usually operated by engine companies in areas where the height of buildings did not call for the services of an aerial ladder, or in areas that were a distance from the nearest ladder company. It permitted fire departments to provide limited ladder company functions while saving on manpower and the purchase of a separate ladder apparatus.

Ahrens-Fox, well known for their piston pumpers, began producing 75-foot and 85-foot aerial ladders equipped with the air-operated Dahill Hoist in 1923. An interesting innovation available on these units was a double bank arrangement, located adjacent to each other under the aerial ladder, to carry the portable ladders. Up to this time, ladder trucks had single ladder banks. The double bank arrangement allowed for more portable ladders to be carried, and a lower overall height of the

vehicle. On these vehicles, the shaft for the tiller steering wheel did not pass through the rungs of the portable ladders as it did on single bank trucks, and therefore it was not necessary to disconnect the tiller wheel and remove the shaft to get a ladder off the truck.

Although some of the earliest motorized fire apparatus were built on commercially available chassis, the vast majority were built by fire apparatus manufacturers on their own custom-built chassis. A trend began to appear during the early 1920s when numerous commercial vehicle manufacturers started to make their chassis available for fire apparatus manufacturers to mount firefighting bodywork on. This permitted smaller fire apparatus manufacturers to specialize in compartmentation, body design, and firefighting capabilities while using existing vehicle chassis. Generally, such vehicles were less expensive than those that were custom-built from the ground up, and were ideally suited for smaller communities with less active fire departments. This practice also allowed many smaller fire apparatus manufacturers to enter and stay alive in such a small, specialized, limited production environment.

The changeover from chain-driven fire apparatus to power trains that were shaft-driven gained momentum in the mid-1920s, and by the end of the decade this became the standard.

Another milestone in fire apparatus development occurred during 1928, when Pirsch delivered what was probably the first American fire apparatus with an enclosed, custom-built cab. Up to this time, the majority of fire apparatus were constructed with open cabs, primarily for visibility and size-up when approaching the fire scene and to assist in positioning the apparatus at the scene. In addition, these cabs did not have doors, to allow for firefighters in the cab to spring into action as soon as they arrived. The time it took to open cab doors was considered a delay. For the most part, the open cab would continue to appear on the majority of apparatus delivered through the 1950s and later, but a big first step was taken when Pirsch delivered this closed-cab pumper to Monroe, Wisconsin.

Fire apparatus delivered through the late 1920s were equipped with a mixture of both right-hand and left-hand drive; that is, the steering wheel could be on either side depending on the manufacturer or what the individual fire department wanted. By the end of the 1920s, left-hand steering had started to become standard.

At the International Association of Fire Chiefs annual convention in 1929, Mack Trucks introduced an aerial ladder that was raised and lowered through a power-take-off mechanism from the motor. This type of aerial ladder operation, with additions and modifications over the years, would become the standard for aerial ladder operations. Eventually, hydraulic systems, operated through power-take-off, would be developed.

An early Ahrens-Fox aerial ladder, this unit originally served Kansas City and is now collector-owned. Ahrens-Fox introduced the double bank configuration to hold portable ladders, thereby lowering the overall height of the apparatus. Neither the driver or tillerman were afforded the protection of windshields.

Above: Wildwood City, NJ, operated this early motorized American LaFrance tiller. The 1913 model has a 65-foot aerial and has been well preserved.

Right: Many commercial chassis manufacturers made their chassis available to fire apparatus manufacturers to mount their bodywork on. This is a FWD-Oshkosh with Pirsch bodywork that served Golden Valley, MN.

THE DEPRESSION YEARS

When the stock market crashed in 1929, the results had a major, long term effect on most of American industry. Fire apparatus manufacturing was not excepted from this, as many cities and towns felt the financial crunch. For a short time, the industry kept going because of orders placed prior to the crash, but before long, reality caught up. Cities could not afford to meet payroll obligations, much less purchase new equipment. Most money for research and development of new products and innovations dried up, and many manufacturers fought for their very existence. Despite all the doom and gloom of the time period, the fire apparatus industry kept plugging away, and there were even some bright spots.

Factory installed windshields started to become more popular on fire apparatus in the early 1930s. Once considered unnecessary, windshields offered a degree of protection from the elements as well as allowing the driver to see more safely, not having to squint constantly because of the wind hitting his unprotected face.

A hydraulic-mechanical aerial ladder mechanism was introduced by Pirsch in 1931. For the first time, all three aerial ladder functions, raise, rotate, and extend, could be performed by one firefighter. Hydraulic lifting cylinders were used to raise the aerial ladder from its bedded position, while the turntable was rotated and the aerial extended mechanically.

Above left: This beautifully restored 1927 Seagrave pumper typified the classic design of fire apparatus from this era. This pumper originally served in Montreal, Quebec.

Right: Many fire departments had apparatus painted a non-traditional color. While red was the most popular, many shades of red were used. Other popular colors were white and chrome yellow. It is possible to find apparatus painted just about any color imaginable. Vineland, NJ, operated this kelly green 1935 Seagrave pumper.

Below: Hand-cranked sirens were the first sirens mounted on fire apparatus. Their volume was dependent on how fast the handle was turned.

Prior to this, once the aerial was raised, rotation and extension was performed by the muscle power of several firefighters by means of hand-cranking.

Located in Elmira Heights, New York, Ward LaFrance, another major player in the industry, started to construct pumpers on custom-built chassis in 1932.

By the mid-1930s the effects of the Depression had caused orders for new fire apparatus to bottom out and new orders had started to trickle in. Most fire departments had entered the Depression with early motorized apparatus and by this time these vehicles were beginning to reach the end of their useful life span. Replacement was necessary.

Some cities, most notably Milwaukee, Jersey City, and New York, took it upon themselves to construct their own apparatus in an attempt to produce new vehicles at less cost. Many fire departments rebuilt apparatus and converted vehicles for other purposes, stretching their resources as much as possible.

Many fire departments created hybrid ladder trucks by placing new or different tractors under older trailers. This was less expensive than purchasing the entire vehicle and was an excellent use of limited resources. This practice continues and is very popular today, with vehicles being refurbished at an unprecedented rate.

Pirsch followed the recent introduction of their innovative aerial mechanism with the production of the first 100-foot aerial ladder to be built in the United States. The aerial was a three-section unit constructed of metal and had hand rails on all three sections. Prior aerial ladders were constructed of wood and were generally 65, 75, or 85-foot models, although some shorter aerials had been produced. This tillered unit was delivered to Melrose, Massachusetts, in 1935. It would take a while, but metal would eventually replace wood in aerial ladder construction. Seagrave also introduced a metal aerial ladder the same year, a 65-foot model. These were mounted on

city service truck chassis and therefore were called service aerials. The introduction of metal aerial ladders was the death knell for water towers. Although ladder pipes, large portable nozzles similar to deck pipes but attached to upper rungs of the aerial, had been introduced to a limited degree on wood aerials, the strength inherent in metal aerial ladder construction readily lent itself to ladder pipe use, negating the need for separate water tower apparatus.

In the mid-1930s and for a short period of time thereafter, a limited movement towards fully enclosed apparatus took place. Several different pumper designs were produced that provided enclosed riding positions for all firefighters on

the apparatus. The first enclosed pumper was built by Mack for Chanloite, North Carolina, in 1935. Several manufacturers constructed enclosed sedan cab style pumpers. This design included a completely enclosed rear body with a roof over the hose bed and windows in the side panels. Bench seating for the firefighters was included inside this enclosure. While being a significant development from a safety standpoint, this concept was ahead of its time and didn't catch on until the civil disturbances of the 1960s forced many fire departments to reinvent it.

In 1938, American LaFrance joined other manufacturers in offering hydraulically operated aerial ladders. However,

Ward LaFrance started constructing fire apparatus in 1932. This 1937 Ward LaFrance 600 gpm pumper served Newville, PA.

Melrose, MA, took delivery of the first 100-foot metal aerial ladder constructed in the United States. It was constructed by Pirsch in 1935 and had a three-section ladder, which made for a long vehicle.

American LaFrance's 100-foot aerials differed from the other manufacturers in that they were four-section instead of three. This permitted a shorter overall length when retracted, allowing the tiller seat and wheel to be permanently fixed. Because of the longer length of other aerial ladders, their tiller seats, wheels, and windshield if any, had to be folded out of the way or disassembled upon arrival at the fire, before the aerial could be raised.

Fire apparatus began to become somewhat enclosed in the late 1930s with the introduction of half doors to open cab models. These doors offered a better degree of protection to those in the cab while still affording the maximum visibility provided by the open cab.

The last water tower to be constructed, a 1938 American LaFrance 65-foot model, was delivered to Los Angeles,

California. The introduction of ladder pipes, especially on the newer metal aerials, would make the water tower obsolete. However, this type of vehicle would remain on the roster of many fire departments for quite some time.

The heavy rescue truck began to come of age in the late 1930s. Up to this time, rescue trucks, sometimes called rescue squads, were generally the size of hose wagons. They were usually equipped with two rows of bench seats in the rear body. The specialized equipment was carried outside, mounted on the running boards or in the open body. But this began to change when several manufacturers constructed fully enclosed van style vehicles that included seating for all firefighters inside the body and equipment was carried either inside the body or in compartments. The most common design was known as the walk-through design, where it was

Left: Fully enclosed safety sedan pumpers, providing enclosed, seated positions for all assigned firefighters, were introduced during the 1930s but were not produced in great numbers. Brookline, MA, operated this 1938 American LaFrance.

Below: American LaFrance produced four-section aerials with a fixed tiller position, resulting in an overall shorter apparatus. This 1940 American LaFrance tiller served Wildwood, NJ.

American LaFrance started a revolution in fire apparatus design with the introduction of a cab-forward aerial ladder chassis in 1939. The J-O-X model, known affectionately as the "Ugly American" set the pace for the entire fire apparatus industry.

possible to enter the body at the rear or through the cab doors and exit at the opposite end of the vehicle. Interior seating was provided on bench seats either against one wall or on both sides of the body.

The next revolution in fire apparatus design was begun in 1939 when American LaFrance introduced the first cab-forward chassis. These vehicles had their cabs located ahead of the engine instead of behind it as in the conventional design. Cab-forward chassis would eventually be used for the majority of custom-built fire apparatus. Known as the J-O-X model,

and popularly nicknamed the "Ugly American," this design was marketed as four-wheel service aerials, and had an extra wide cab when compared to other apparatus of that time. The cab-forward design provided much better visibility for the driver while also having a better turning radius.

Another innovation that was introduced to the fire service during 1939 was the diesel engine. The first diesel powered pumper was constructed by the New Stutz Fire Engine Company, using a Cummins diesel. Eventually, every piece of fire apparatus constructed in the United States would be diesel powered, but diesels would not begin to appear in large numbers until the 1960s.

While the quad had four distinct functions, pumper, hose wagon, booster unit, and service ladder, another new type of apparatus began to appear in the late 1930s that incorporated a fifth function. The quint, in addition to providing the four functions of the quad and being built on the same style chassis, had the added capability of being equipped with an aerial ladder. This vehicle was utilized in the same capacity as the quad, in less active areas remote from ladder companies, and provided both

engine and ladder company functions to a limited degree. Sometimes marketed as a "one truck fire department," such vehicles could not carry everything that was required by separate vehicles with individual functions. Often, optimum positioning at fires could not be achieved because of conflicting functions. Sometimes the aerial ladder needed to be used for rescue while at the same time it was necessary to hook-up to a hydrant and supply water. This could only be accomplished simultaneously if the hydrant was exactly where the need for the aerial ladder was. Nevertheless, such vehicles did fill a void for certain departments.

This pumper, built by the New Stutz Fire Engine Company and delivered to Columbus, IN, was powered by a Cummins diesel engine. This was the first diesel powered fire apparatus in the United States and was ahead of its time. Diesels were not fully accepted into the fire service until the 1960s.

Right: The addition of an aerial ladder onto a quad gave that vehicle a fifth function. The quint provided a pump, hose, booster equipment, portable ladders and an aerial ladder, all on the same apparatus. While limited in operational effectiveness, this type vehicle did provide the basics of each function.

Right: Hand painted murals, gold leaf striping, stained wood, and other custom accessories were common on fire apparatus of the 1920s and 1930s.

Far right: Early motorized apparatus had exposed intake and discharge valves. Newer units have as much of these fittings as possible behind bodywork panels.

Page 37: Deckpipes from hose wagons and a water tower deliver heavy caliber streams at a five-alarm building fire on New York's waterfront.

THE WAR YEARS

Above right: Fire apparatus built on military-style chassis were constructed at an unprecedented rate during World War II. This 1941 Chevrolet was utilized by the U.S. Army as an early airfield fire apparatus.

By the 1940s, it appeared that most of the apparatus manufacturers had rebounded from the Depression. Many fire departments were unable to purchase new apparatus during the Depression years, and their fleets were old and worn out. Apparatus manufacturers were working at capacity to replace these vehicles. At the same time, the rest of America's industrial base was working at near capacity producing materials for World War II.

Once America entered the war, all manufacturing was directed at the war effort. The use of many materials was restricted. Fire apparatus were considered essential to the war effort and production continued but most apparatus built were earmarked for military use. Procurement of apparatus by municipalities was very limited and had to be justified and then approved by the government. Several fire apparatus manufacturers also built military vehicles, aircraft parts, guns, and other necessary items. Due to restrictions on certain materials, fire apparatus built during this time appeared rather bland, having no chrome parts or brightwork. To avoid confusion with air raid sirens, the use of sirens on emergency vehicles was prohibited in most large cities.

Instead, apparatus were equipped with shrill sounding exhaust whistles, the Buckeye whistle being very popular.

Some major developments came out of the war years. The fear of air raids led to the production of various styles of trailer pumps. These self-contained two- and four-wheel trailers could be towed behind any vehicle and were capable of getting a hose stream into operation. They were generally manned by civilian defense volunteers and were a big supplement to the existing firefighting forces. Purpose-built airport crash apparatus, primarily developed as a result of the development of larger military aircraft, began to appear in large numbers. Following the war, many of these vehicles were recycled to the large number of civilian airports that were rapidly coming on line. The use of high pressure fog for firefighting was pioneered by the U.S. Navy for shipboard use. This principal could be adopted to a limited degree in struc-tural firefighting and high pressure fog pumpers were developed. The John Bean Division of FMC was one of the largest producers of such vehicles. Many unusual apparatus were constructed or converted from other vehicles to provide for special wartime demands.

The war didn't interfere with apparatus design, as two of the most well known apparatus chassis were developed during that time. In 1940, Mack introduced their L-model chassis, which gained widespread use for almost every type of apparatus over the next 13 years. During the war, American LaFrance polled fire chiefs to determine what style apparatus they wanted produced. The result was American LaFrance's 700 Series, probably one of the most esthetically pleasing and most popular fire apparatus. Full size mock-ups were constructed during the war, and production started after the war ended. An interesting side note to the development of the 700 Series is that

This former U.S. Army aircraft crash rescue truck was built in 1943 and readily shows the technological advances rapidly made in this field in the two years since the apparatus shown on the previous page was constructed. It is shown in service at Islip-MacArthur Airport in NY.

The Mack L-model was introduced at the beginning of World War II and became one of the most popular fire apparatus chassis. This unit is a 1949 750 gpm pumper that served Milwaukee, WI.

one of the mock-ups that was constructed was of a rear-mounted aerial. This design was rejected as impractical, but over twenty years later would be re-introduced and become a rapidly selling model, eventually replacing the majority of tiller units. The 700 Series sold in great numbers and became a symbol of American fire apparatus.

Another area that directly developed from wartime technology was airport crash apparatus. Carbon dioxide was found to be an effective extinguishing agent for aircraft fires in this time period. Crash apparatus were developed that carried a

large quantity of this extinguishing agent, along with hose reels and special applicators, and in many cases, booms that could be extended out over burning aircraft from which carbon dioxide could be applied. A specialized firm, Cardox, built many of these units.

Advances in two-way radio technology also resulted from the war, and it wasn't long before fire departments realized the great advantages that two-way radio communications afforded. Apparatus so equipped had far greater mobility. Without radios, once an apparatus left the fire station, it was out of contact until

Right: For years, many volunteer fire department apparatus carried turnout gear and helmets exposed, readily available to volunteer firefighters arriving at the scene.

Left: By the end of World War II, aircraft crash fire rescue had developed greatly. Units capable of delivering carbon dioxide onto burning aircraft were state-of-the-art. This U.S.A.F. O-6 model protected Hickam Field in Hawaii.

European fire apparatus design differed greatly from fire apparatus built in the United States. This "turntable ladder" is unusual in that it is a Metz aerial mounted on a Dennis chassis. Rear-mounted aerial ladders were common in Europe for decades before they were introduced in America. This style vehicle was popular in England following World War II.

Many fire departments made do with the apparatus in service at the start of World War II as wartime restrictions prevented the purchase of new apparatus. Most new apparatus went to the military. As quickly as possible following the war, new apparatus was procured by many fire departments. This 100-foot Seagrave tiller was typical of those produced towards the end of and immediately following the war.

GROWTH AND EXPANSION

The large numbers of rugged surplus military vehicles available following World War II made for affordable, practical conversions into firefighting vehicles. Folsom, NJ, operated this former military 1942 Dodge that was converted for firefighting in the pine barrens.

Following World War II, in addition to pumpers and aircraft crash units, a great number of standard military vehicles became surplus and were obtained by fire departments. Many were converted into brush and forestry units by the addition of pumps, tanks, and other equipment. The bodywork on these varied from having full pumper bodies constructed, to only adding essential equipment. Some

very interesting conversions resulted. Military tankers were easily converted for fire service use. Most of these converted military vehicles were utilized by rural fire departments. Among the more interesting conversions were half-tracks and armored cars, mostly into forestry units for off-road use, and amphibious vehicles to perform the functions of fireboats. Conversion of surplus military vehicles into firefighting units

has continued to the present time, although it is not as widespread as it was after World War II.

Maxim entered the aerial ladder market in 1947 when production started on their own metal aerial ladder design. Mack Trucks would form an alliance with Maxim to utilize Maxim's aerial ladder on Mack chassis. Mack aggressively marketed these units and many different models of Mack fire apparatus equipped with Maxim aerials were constructed over the years.

The Crown Coach Corporation, a manufacturer of buses, constructed its first fire truck, a pumper, in 1949. It was an open cab, cab-forward model that bore a striking resemblance to the fronts of the buses that this firm produced. The Crown Firecoach design was extremely popular on the West Coast, with the Los Angeles City and County Fire Departments being major users of this brand.

To celebrate its 70th anniversary of building fire apparatus, Seagrave introduced an upgraded, more modern cab design during 1951. This model was characterized by a wide front grille and by having the siren recessed into the nose of its hood. The front fenders were larger and gave the apparatus a much bigger appearance than earlier models. The headlights were built into the fenders on this new model, which was called the 70th Anniversary Model.

Seagrave gambled that most fire departments would still prefer a conventional design over the cab-forward design recently introduced by other manufacturers. While many departments did order this style, the cab-forward models would eventually dominate the market. This would be Seagrave's last conventional cab design and, with some minor design modifications, would remain in production for almost twenty years.

Partly as a result of the military build-up for the Korean War, but mainly because of the increased size of aircraft, the United States Air Force had a need for a larger capacity crash rescue vehicle. As a result, American LaFrance was awarded a contract which resulted in the construction of over 1100 O-10 and O-11 model crash trucks. These vehicles were the first

Above left: Philadelphia converted this former military half-track for off-road brush fire operations. Surplus military vehicles of all kinds received a new lease on life in the fire service.

Many large cities acquired as many new apparatus as possible following World War II. Milwaukee operated a fleet of 85-foot tillered Pirsch aerial ladders similar to this unit. Ladder 16 is a 1949 model.

Maxim introduced a metal aerial ladder of its own design in 1947. The Maxim ladder was delivered throughout the country but was particularly popular in the Middle Atlantic and New England states.

mass produced airport crash apparatus and incorporated state-of-the-art technology. They were designed to be air-transportable for rapid forward deployment and capable of going into operation on arrival. Equipped with crew cabs, remote-controlled roof-mounted foam turrets, pump-and-roll capability, and swing-out hose reels, they proved effective for their intended mission. These vehicles became standard fixtures at every United States air base worldwide.

In 1952, Maxim constructed a rear-mounted aerial ladder truck using a German-built Magirus aerial mounted on a con-ventional engine-ahead pumper chassis. The idea was still ahead of its time and only a handful were sold over the next few years. The following year, Maxim introduced an airport crash vehicle built on an off-road Walter chassis. It was equipped with foam turrets mounted on a rooftop platform built over the cab, and wide flotation tires for off-runway operation. This model and its refined versions would become a popular choice for civilian airports. As the size of aircraft, along with the fuel load carried increased, nurse tankers were added to accompany and resupply airport crash apparatus operating at aircraft incidents.

Mack introduced a restyled cab in 1954 with the introduction of its B-model. This chassis replaced the popular L-model, but was just as popular. Its cab design had more streamlined, rounded lines and this chassis was utilized for all types of fire apparatus.

In 1955, New York City accepted the last wood aerials to be built. FWD delivered 25 open-cab, tillered, 75-foot wood aerials to New York, closing another chapter in fire apparatus history. These aerials were constructed of Douglas Fir, laminated for additional strength. During the same year, a low-priced electrically operated aerial ladder was introduced by Memco. This small aerial was available to many fire apparatus builders and could be mounted on most chassis. Its unusual appearance made for some curious-looking vehicles.

Ahrens-Fox, now merged with C.D. Beck, a bus manufacturer, introduced its own rounded cab-forward design in

1956. This cab was in such demand that when Beck was acquired by Mack this chassis was continued in production, marketed as Mack's C-model. In addition to those produced by Ahrens-Fox and Mack, a handful of similar cabs were produced by Approved Fire Apparatus, a small builder located in Long Island, New York.

Ford introduced its popular tilt-cab design in 1957. Designated as its C-series, this chassis has probably been used for more fire apparatus than any other commercial truck chassis. This cab was built by the Budd Company and was also utilized by other manufacturers, including Mack. Several modifications and design changes have been made to it over the years and it has been produced in canopy cab and even customized crew cab versions. Virtually every fire apparatus manufacturer has built bodywork that was mounted on this chassis.

The Maxim aerial ladder was also aggressively marketed by Mack Trucks, mounted on various model Mack chassis. West Hempstead, NY, utilized this 75-foot Maxim aerial mounted on a 1950 Mack L-model chassis.

Crown, a bus manufacturer, entered the fire apparatus market with a cab-forward design called the Firecoach. Crown apparatus was very popular on the West Coast, with both Los Angeles City and County operating large fleets. This unit, originally a high pressure unit, has been converted into a foam carrier.

Left: To celebrate its 70th anniversary, in 1951 Seagrave introduced a newly styled conventional cab model called the 70th Anniversary Model. This cab design was marketed on pumpers, aerials, rescue trucks, and special units. Detroit operated a fleet of Anniversary Series sedan cab pumpers.

Right: To keep pace with larger aircraft being constructed as well as to provide fire protection during the Cold War buildup, American LaFrance constructed over 1100 O-10 and O-11 aircraft crash rescue vehicles for the U.S.A.F. This is an O-11A built in 1952.

Fire protection at civilian airfields was also changing. The first generation of civilian aircraft crash rescue vehicles included this type built on a 1949 Walter chassis.

Nurse tankers were used to resupply primary crash rescue vehicles at aircraft crash operations. These units would replenish the crash vehicles to sustain continued operations following the initial application of foam.

Above: Despite the fact that metal aerials had been available for some time, both New York and Chicago continued to purchase wooden aerial ladders. The last wood aerials manufactured was an order of 25 FWD 75-foot units delivered to New York City during 1955.

Left: Mack replaced its popular L-model chassis with the B-model during 1954. The B-model proved to be as popular as the L-model. Chicago's Engine 60 operated with a 1956 B-model 1000 gpm pumper.

it returned. If responding to an alarm, all apparatus responding had to reach the scene. There was no way to return unneeded units until they arrived at the scene, and then, if not needed, they had to return quickly to the fire station to be available for the next alarm. During this time away from the fire station, they could not be redeployed to a subsequent alarm. Radios gave the fire service this flexibility, and also allowed fire companies to perform in-service fire prevention inspections, pre-fire planning, and training at locations away from the fire station. Early

radios were quite large and bulky, often taking up a small compartment or the area under the bench seat in the cab.

At the end of the war, many fire departments still operated the same fire apparatus with which they had entered the Depression years. The lack of money during the Depression did not permit replacement, but then wartime restrictions further complicated this situation. So many apparatus needed to be replaced that manufacturers had a difficult time keeping up with the demand

Perhaps the apparatus design that is the icon for American fire apparatus of the 1940s and 1950s, the American LaFrance 700 Series was developed during World War II and went into production immediately following the end of the war.

Left: This cab-forward fire apparatus design was originally developed by Ahrens-Fox under Beck ownership. Approved Fire Apparatus also built several units using the same design. Less than twenty were built before Mack Trucks purchased Beck, along with the rights to this cab design. Mack marketed it as the C-model. This 1956 Ahrens-Fox was in service in Hempstead, NY.

Right: Engine 270's 1958 Mack was one of a large fleet of C-models to serve New York City.

Page 57: One of three Super Pumper System satellite hose wagons, all built on Mack C-model chassis, operates its oversize deck gun at a fire in Brooklyn, NY.

Left: Ford introduced this style cab-over-engine design in 1957. Designated the C Series, it is probably the most popular chassis on which fire apparatus manufacturers mount their bodywork. Jericho, NY, operated this unusual model with American LaFrance bodywork. The pump panel is located on the "wrong side," that is on the side away from the driver, on this unit.

Right: Surplus military vehicles, because of their ruggedness, low mileage, and upkeep, continue to make excellent conversions into fire apparatus. This 1959 Dodge has been outfitted into a brush fire unit by the Oceanic Hook & Ladder Company on Staten Island, NY.

INNOVATIONS

Up to this time, fire apparatus, as with all heavy trucks, were generally equipped with manual shift transmissions. In 1957, Mack made available an automatic transmission for fire service use. Another ten years or so would pass before such transmissions would receive widespread use, but today, virtually all fire apparatus constructed are so equipped.

One of the most important developments in fire apparatus history took place in Chicago during 1958. Chicago's fire commissioner had observed a utility crew at work in an elevated bucket truck. Seeing the advantages of such equipment for fire service use, a 50-foot articulated boom was purchased from Pitman and mounted on a GMC chassis. The Chicago Fire

Department shops outfitted the basket with a monitor nozzle, attached hose alongside the boom, and coined the term "Snorkel." The rest is history. This conversion revolutionized firefighting tactics, allowing for pinpoint accuracy in applying elevated streams, a stable platform from which to perform ventilation and other tasks, and an easier, less stressful method of removing trapped or injured victims. The first Snorkel was very crude in appearance, but lessons learned from its fireground performance rapidly led to refinements in design and components and an extremely useful piece of equipment was added to the fire service inventory. At first, elevating platforms functioned as special units but, eventually, most fire departments began assigning them as regular apparatus of ladder companies.

Above left: The first fire service elevating platform was created by Chicago's fire commissioner at the time, who got the idea after seeing a utility crew at work. The 50-foot Pitman boom was mounted on a 1958 GMC chassis and outfitted by the fire department shops. This crude conversion quickly proved itself under fire conditions.

Cab-forward apparatus chassis were becoming more popular and demand for them was increasing. In response, Seagrave, Maxim, and FWD all introduced cabs of this design during 1959, but all continued to market their conventional cab models as well. FWD's cab-forward model was actually built by Truck Cab Manufacturers of Cincinnati. This model, known as the Cincinnati Cab, was supplied to many different fire apparatus builders and appears with many different builder's plates mounted to it. During the same year, Hi-Ranger entered the elevating platform field, marketing a boom of open truss construction, much boxier in appearance than the earlier Pitman boom. Other manufacturers followed with several different boom designs.

Also in 1959, Saulsbury Fire Apparatus built their first vehicle, a tanker. In 1967, Saulsbury would built its first rescue truck. Saulsbury would become a major force in the fire apparatus industry, specializing in high quality heavy rescue trucks and similar vehicles, but also constructing pumpers and all other types of fire apparatus.

Above: Cab-forward chassis for fire-fighting vehicles were becoming more popular because of their visibility and maneuverability. Seagrave introduced both open and closed cab models in 1959.

Right: Most of the major apparatus manufacturers introduced cab-forward models to compete for the demand. This Maxim served in Indianapolis as Engine 6.

In the late 1950s and early 1960s, a small trend developed in the number of rear-mounted aerial ladder trucks delivered. This trend only lasted a few years, but saw Magirus and Geesink rear-mounted aerials delivered on FWD, Mack, Maxim, and Seagrave chassis. It would still be a few more years before these compact, shorter ladder trucks would become commonplace.

The late 1950s also saw the introduction of the air horn on fire apparatus. This was a natural extension of the pneumatic brake systems that were becoming popular. The air horn added to the audible warning capability of the apparatus, and many feel eventually replaced the bell.

American LaFrance experimented with jet engine powered fire apparatus for a short time beginning in 1960. Several apparatus were constructed that were powered by Boeing gas turbine engines. These vehicles, which included a pumper for San Francisco, a pumper for Mount Vernon, Virginia, and a tiller for Seattle, were designated the Turbo-Chief series, and were characterized by the large stainless steel exhaust stack coming from the engine compartment. Unfortunately, these units proved to be extremely noisy, sluggish, and maintenance intensive in actual service. All were retrofitted with conventional power plants within a short time.

Two additional manufacturers began marketing cab-forward apparatus during 1960. Ward LaFrance introduced its flat-faced Firebrand model while Walter introduced an airport crash rescue vehicle chassis of this design.

Electronic sirens began to appear on fire apparatus during the early 1960s. At first, these were installed in addition to the older, louder mechanical sirens. Eventually, in many cases, the electronics took the place of the mechanical models. Often, this was brought about as a reaction to environmentalists' complaints of excessive noise. However, mechanical sirens are now making a comeback, to supplement the quieter

FWD's cab-forward model was built by Truck Cab Manufacturers of Cincinnati and was known in the industry as the "Cincinnati Cab." This cab was available to other manufacturers as well. Detroit's 85-foot Snorkel shows evident design improvement when compared to Chicago's first Snorkel.

electronic ones. Over the years, sound proofing in automobiles, coupled with auto entertainment systems, has severely limited the effectiveness of the electronic models.

Also during the early 1960s, Mack Trucks began to aggressively market diesel powered fire apparatus. The diesel was touted to be more cost effective to operate, provide better mileage, and require less maintenance. By the mid-1960s, diesel powered apparatus was beginning to become commonplace. Today, diesel power is standard for fire apparatus.

American LaFrance added two new special purpose vehicles to its product line during 1962: the Aero-Chief, an articulated boom elevating platform, and the Airport-Chief, a custom-built, four-wheel-drive airport unit. Another large airport crash vehicle entered the U.S. Air Force inventory that year. Built by FWD on an eight-wheel-drive chassis, the new P-2 was developed to cope better with the larger bombers and transports being made. This boxy vehicle was designed for rapid acceleration and all-terrain maneuverability. It carried

2,300 gallons of water and 200 gallons of foam, and had pump-and-roll capability.

Competition in apparatus design was resulting in rapid change. A telescopic elevating platform of aluminum truss construction was introduced by Sutphen while Seagrave presented its own creation, the Eagle Rescue boom, in 1963. Mack Trucks entered the elevating platform field in 1964 with its Aerialscope design, a solid telescopic boom. The first few of this model boom were constructed by Truco and Eaton, but Baker Equipment Engineering took over shortly thereafter and has been building the Aerialscope since. The same year American LaFrance began to build its Pioneer model, a low-cost custom-built unit with a flat front and inverted windshield design.

After several years of planning, design, and construction, New York City took delivery of its famous Super Pumper System in 1965. Originally designed as a "land fireboat" based on two Mack tractor trailers, one a massive pumper, the

With the Pitman Snorkel boom proving its advantages to the fire service, other elevating platform boom manufacturers began to introduce their products. Among these was Hi-Ranger, with a boom of open truss construction.

Left: A short period of experimentation with rear-mounted aerial ladders took place during the early 1960s. Milwaukee operated this 1961 FWD equipped with an 85-foot Geesink aerial.

Right: Both Chicago and New York tried German-built Magirus aerials on rear-mounted chassis. Chicago's Ladder 8 operated this 144-foot Magirus built on a 1960 Mack chassis. Among the problems encountered with these units was the lack of space to properly carry the firefighters, portable ladders, and other equipment normally carried by American ladder companies.

other a hose wagon, when actually delivered the final product consisted of these two plus an additional three standard "satellite" hose wagons. The original concept was to have the tractor trailer hose tender carry its large diameter hose on huge reels, but several factors prevented this design and the three satellites were included to enable the system to carry the specified amount of hose. The pumper was capable of supplying 10,000 gpm of water, the most powerful land-based pumping equipment, equal to ten conventional pumpers. The tender and satellites were equipped with large deck pipes. The concept was a sound one, but limited in application. The most-used components of the system became the three satellites, because of their size, maneuverability, and faster response than the larger pumper and tender. Eventually, the Super Pumper and Tender were retired, replaced by six conventional 2,000 gpm pumpers geographically dispersed and paired to operate with six satellite hose wagons. While in service, the Super Pumper System put on awesome demonstrations of its firefighting capabilities at the city's major fires.

Above: American LaFrance experimented with jet engines to power fire apparatus. Unfortunately, these units were noisy, slow to accelerate, and maintenance intensive. They were characterized by a large exhaust stack coming from the engine.

Right: Ward LaFrance marketed its Firebrand model to compete with other manufacturers offering cab-forward chassis. This 1962 1000 gpm pumper served as Engine 23 in Buffalo, NY.

During the mid-1960s, major cities throughout the nation experienced episodes of violent civil unrest. The riots and resulting fires severely overtaxed fire departments, but worse, firefighters and their apparatus became targets of the rioters. Fire apparatus was bombarded with bricks, bottles, fire bombs, and even shot at. Firefighters were killed and injured. Most apparatus in service at this time were still open cab units and inner city fire departments reacted by constructing makeshift cabs, roof enclosures over the back steps, enclosed tiller seats, and even individual personnel enclosures that looked like telephone booths on apparatus. Some very

strange-looking apparatus resulted. Many departments purchased enclosed apparatus as quickly as possible. Some departments refused to allow firefighters to ride the back step on pumpers anymore. Exposed tools and equipment were often taken from apparatus by rioters. These events, more than any other single factor, led to the design of crew cabs where all firefighters rode inside and more compartmentation where all tools were carried in locked compartments, and radically changed other features of apparatus construction.

An attention-getting, futuristic cab design, known as the Crusader, was introduced by Young in 1966. The full width,

Even airport crash rescue vehicles were marketed on cab-forward chassis. The Federal Aviation Administration used this 1962 Walter at Atlantic City International Airport in New Jersey.

low profile cab provided a roomier interior for firefighters and its large, low cut windshields provided excellent visibility. This design was the forerunner of the wide style Cincinnati cab that went into production beginning in 1984.

Mack added to the rapidly occurring design changes in the apparatus field when it introduced, in 1966, the MB-model, known as the Post Office truck because of that agency's widespread use of this type. This flat-faced model became a suitable chassis for fire apparatus production, especially for bodywork built by other manufacturers. The following year, Mack added two new models that were destined to become among the most popular fire apparatus chassis. The CF-model, a boxy, cab-forward design replaced the C-model, which was inherited from Beck, and the R-model, a short conventional design, replaced the B-model.

Also in 1967, Seagrave began to market its Rear Admiral, a rear-mounted aerial built on its custom cab-forward chassis. This unit had a 100-foot aerial and a new innovation, four-wheel steering. The driver had the capability of steering the rear wheels from the cab, making this vehicle highly maneuverable in tight, congested street conditions. While several units were built with this feature, the majority of Rear Admirals were equipped with conventional front steering only.

Another design innovation that appeared in 1967 was the top-mounted pump panel. Where formerly the pump operator controlled the pump operation while standing in the street adjacent to the pump panel, this new design, introduced by Howe, placed the operator in a position behind the cab, which afforded a better view of overall operations, but more importantly, provided a far greater degree of safety, removing the possibility of being struck by passing vehicles. As with most new ideas, this one took off gradually, and is still in the process of evolving. Many say that the safety afforded by this design far outweighs any disadvantages, but others, especially those departments serving inner city areas, feel that this position needlessly exposes the pump operator and makes him an easy target.

The following year, American LaFrance introduced its entry into the rear-mounted aerial field, a 100-foot model designated the Ladder-Chief. To keep things interesting, Snorkel introduced a 54-foot articulated boom device, the Squrt, which could be mounted to new pumpers and hose wagons or retrofitted to older ones, providing elevated stream capabilities, similar to the older water towers, at a fraction of the cost of an elevating platform. This device had a remote controlled

Left: American LaFrance introduced its Aero-Chief elevating platform to the fire service during 1962. It was an articulating boom design. This 70-foot model is operated by Tenafly, NJ.

Built by FWD for the U.S.A.F., the P-2 was designed to cope with the larger aircraft entering service. Built on an eight-wheel-drive chassis, it carried 2,300 gallons of water and 200 gallons of foam.

nozzle at its end, not a basket. A telescopic boom model, the Tele-Squrt, would follow in a few years, as would varying boom heights, up to 75 feet. To compete, Ward LaFrance introduced its Command Tower, a telescopic platform that could be mounted to a pumper, reached a height of 22 feet and was equipped with a deck pipe.

The largest elevating platform built for firefighting up to this time was introduced by Calavar, a firm that manufactured elevating platforms to service aircraft, in 1969. Known as the Firebird, this model was produced with combination telescop-

ic-articulating booms up to 150 feet in height, and when set up for operation, was suspended several feet above the ground on outriggers. Because of its large size and the space required for fireground set-up, this model was not sold in large numbers.

The mid- to late 1960s also saw the wide scale introduction of cross-lay hose beds and pre-connected hose lines. Cross-lay hose beds carried hose lines packed from side to side, usually located in the area either ahead of, behind, or atop the pump panel. These hose lines were carried pre-connected to discharge outlets on the pump panel. Up to this time, most hose was car-

Left: Sutphen introduced an elevating platform of open aluminum truss construction that was of a telescopic design known as the aerial tower. Boston operated several Sutphen towers nicknamed BATs for Boston Aerial Tower.

ried in the rear hose beds and was not carried connected to outlets. It was necessary to break the hose line when it was determined that sufficient hose had been stretched and connect it manually to a discharge outlet. Lack of sufficient manpower led to the development of pre-connected lines and different tactics. On arrival, the pumper would either work off its booster tank until supplied by another unit or drop a firefighter with a supply line at a hydrant as it approached the fire building. Rather than positioning at the hydrant and stretching hose line to the fire, the pumper would proceed to the fire, using the apparatus to stretch a large diameter supply line. The pumper would then position as close as possible to the fire building and firefighters would stretch the pre-connected lines into the building. This was an efficient operation with less manpower but was only adequate for smaller structures such as dwellings. The smaller diameter pre-connected lines could not supply adequate water and were not long enough to operate in larger commercial structures or multi-story apartment houses.

Right: Following World War II, most European fire apparatus was standardized in design and equipment carried. This 1960 Magirus, built in Germany, is rather plain in appearance when compared to American apparatus of the era.

Seagrave attempted to compete in the elevating platform market by introducing a boom of its own design, known as the Eagle Rescue boom. This model, built in 1963, saw service in Nashville, TN. Only a small number of these units was constructed.

Made popular by New York City's widespread use of them, the Baker Aerialscope was first introduced in 1964 by Mack with the boom actually built by Truco. Tower-Ladder 1 proved the usefulness of this boom by responding to major fires throughout the city for several years, until additional towers were purchased.

New York's Super Pumper was the most powerful land based pumper ever constructed. It was capable of pumping over 10,000 gpm at full capacity. It was built by Mack and placed into service during 1965.

This vehicle operated as the hose tender for the Super Pumper, carrying the large diameter hose, fittings, and deck pipe. Both vehicles responded together as a unit.

Page 75: One of the earliest Aerialscopes constructed, built on a Mack C-model chassis, operates its elevated stream into a burning warehouse in Brooklyn, NY.

Left: Firefighters riding open apparatus became easy targets during the civil disturbances of the 1960s. Major cities scurried to outfit these open vehicles with makeshift protective coverings, often resulting in very strange-looking apparatus such as this 1962 Ward LaFrance pumper in Boston.

Right: Many fire departments were still operating apparatus built during the 1940s when they were suddenly in the midst of the civil disturbances of the 1960s. A 1947 Seagrave pumper in Elizabeth, NJ, was among many vintage units equipped with makeshift protective covering.

Left: New York outfitted almost its entire fleet with protective makeshift cabs. Only a small percentage had closed cabs. This 1953 American LaFrance tiller has had a plywood enclosure fitted over the cab as well as over the tillerman's position.

Right: Harrisburg, PA, opted to install plexiglass on angle iron framework to protect the firefighters riding this 1951 Mack.

The rapid redesigning of new apparatus so that all firefighters could ride inside also resulted in some strange vehicles until a practical compromise between functional design and appearance was struck. New York's first crew cabs were five of these 1969 Mack custom-built RF models.

Cincinnati purchased several Seagrave pumpers and tillers that appeared to have design characteristics of armored cars. Jump seat windows were omitted, and all equipment was carried inside compartments. The roof extended completely over the hose bed on these pumpers.

Young introduced its Crusader cab, designed with input from firefighters. The futuristic design offered excellent visibility and extra room inside the full width cab.

Known as the "Post Office" cab because of the Postal Service's widespread use of this chassis, the Mack MB model proved very popular for fire apparatus. Chicago's Snorkel Squad 1 was a 1966 model equipped with a 50-foot Pitman Snorkel.

Left: The Mack CF chassis was introduced in 1967 to replace the C-model. The CF was extremely popular with the fire service, especially in the Northeast, and is still in great demand on refurbished apparatus.

Right: The Mack R-model replaced the popular B-model. Its short wheelbase made it a logical choice for pumpers in older cities with tight, congested streets. Pittsburgh Engine 4 was one of several that served that city.

When Seagrave began to market rear-mounted aerials, known as the Rear Admiral, it offered a rear steering option that enabled the driver to steer the rear wheels when required in congested situations. Chicago's Ladder 20 operated with this 1969 Seagrave 100-foot rear-mount.

The Mack CF chassis was utilized for pumpers, tankers, Aerialscopes, Snorkels, rear-mounts, straight frame aerials, tillers, rescues, special units, and aerial ladder tractors. This 75-foot Baker Aerialscope was mounted on a Mack CF chassis.

Above: The top-mounted pump control panel was introduced in 1967 by Howe. This design allowed the pump operator to be in an elevated position out of traffic and more able to see the entire fireground operations. However, in the inner city areas, it also exposed the operator and made him more of a target.

Above right: Fort Lee, NJ, operated one of the earliest Howe pumpers constructed with top-mounted pump controls.

Right: American LaFrance's entry into the rear-mount field was its Ladder Chief. New York operated this 1969 100-foot model that was originally built as a demonstrator.

Right: Snorkel began marketing an articulated elevated stream device, known as the Squrt, in 1968. This boom was intended for tactical applications where water application was needed but it was not necessary to have a manned elevating platform perform the task. These booms were mounted on new pumpers as well as being retrofitted to older apparatus. Some departments, like Columbus, OH, used Squrts mounted on hose wagons or other special apparatus used mainly to supply the elevated stream.

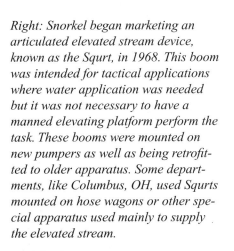

Left: Snorkel followed the Squrt with a telescopic model, the Tele-Squrt. This Tele-Squrt was retrofitted onto one of New York's 1970 Mack pumpers, replacing a damaged Squrt.

Right: Ward LaFrance designed its Command Tower, a platform which extended 22 feet, to provide an elevated position from which to use the deck pipe.

Below: Among the largest fire service elevating booms was the Calavar Firebird. The boom was an articulating design, but each section also telescoped, with models up to 150 feet in height available.

Left: Following the trend of other manufacturers, Pirsch also made available a cab-forward design. This 1963 Pirsch cab-forward pumper served Milwaukee.

Below: The American LaFrance Pioneer model was offered as a lower cost alternative to their custom line. Pumpers built on this chassis were common but only a handful of aerial ladders were built on this chassis. Pittsburgh operated this 1973 Pioneer tiller.

Above: Even after Seagrave introduced its cab-forward model, production continued on conventional cab models, giving fire departments an option. In addition, Seagrave offered its tiller position as either a permanent fixed position or a removable, over-the-ladder position as on this 100-foot Baltimore City aerial.

Right: The design of fire apparatus in Australia is a cross between European and American engineering and construction. This pumper, operated by the South Australian Metropolitan Fire Service, was built by Mills Tui, with Darley components on an International chassis.

YEARS OF CHANGE

In the early 1970s, Ward LaFrance created what was probably the most emotional and controversial issue ever to hit the fire apparatus field. By aggressively marketing a new color for fire apparatus, lime-green, as being more visible and therefore safer, a wedge was driven into the fire service. Traditionalists stood behind the old standard red, while "progressive" fire service personnel preached the advantages of the new color. At one point, there were actually more apparatus being delivered in the new color than the traditional red. Many fire departments, large and small, switched to the new color. But after about a decade, many departments began going back to red. Many apparatus were repainted. Virtually every major department that had gone to the new color returned to traditional red. Currently, few new apparatus are

Ward LaFrance started a heated debate in the fire service by marketing the color lime-green as being more visible, hence safer, for fire apparatus. While many fire departments switched to the new color, most have returned to traditional red.

delivered in the lime-green color. While no one reason can be pinpointed for the return to red, many factors contributed to it. Probably the most important factor was the new color's lack of recognition as that of a fire truck. The vast majority of people have been conditioned to believe from early childhood that fire engines are red. The lack of recognition of the new color was documented as a contributing factor in accidents involving lime-green apparatus. Other factors included poor morale of firefighters assigned to these vehicles and the appearance of lime-green apparatus. It seemed that after initial delivery, keeping up the shiny, bright appearance of this color was not as easy to keep up as red, and these vehicles didn't instill the pride that the traditionally painted trucks had in the fire service. While some may argue that these were unjustified rea-

After running a controlled pilot program using lime-green apparatus and analyzing the results, New York City opted to change from all-red to white-over-red apparatus with more warning lights.

sons, nevertheless, they were factors. Perhaps the most important reason, however, was a controlled pilot program that took place over a period of several years in a major city that was considering changing to lime-green. Several lime-green apparatus were purchased, and a control group of red apparatus responding to the same alarms was established. The end result: the lime-green apparatus were involved in accidents more often than the red ones in this pilot program.

Beginning in 1972, Syracuse, New York, started using an innovative concept for its engine companies. In addition to a standard pumper, each engine company was assigned a mini-pumper. These were small, lightweight vehicles with small pumps, booster tank, pre-connected lines and limited equipment. These units were staffed by two firefighters from the

associated engine company and could handle the majority of routine calls, car fires, outside rubbish fires, brush fires, and similar incidents. When responding to this type of call, they responded alone, leaving the pumper and the balance of the crew in the firehouse available for a subsequent alarm. They were particularly effective in getting into the many multi-level parking garages in the city. When responding to structural fires, both the mini-pumper and standard pumper responded. The mini-pumper was often able to arrive at the scene more quickly, position closer to the fire building, and initiate a faster interior attack utilizing its pre-connected lines and booster tank. The standard pumper would then supply water to the mini-pumper on its arrival. In addition to these tactical advantages, the mini-pumpers were less expensive to purchase and operate than the standard pumpers, and dispatching them on the majority of routine responses saved wear and tear on and prolonged the service life of the standard pumpers.

Above: Syracuse, NY, pioneered the mini-pumper concept, using small, fast, highly maneuverable pumpers that could arrive and commence firefighting more quickly than standard pumpers. In a sense, this was the same tactic used by horse-drawn chemical wagons while waiting for steamers to get into operation.

Left: Grove produced an aerial tower that was a departure from existing models in that it was a heavy-duty aerial ladder with a bucket attached to the top fly section of the ladder.

LTI acquired Grove in 1974 and continued the Ladder Tower in production. This 85-foot tower was built in 1976 on a Seagrave chassis.

Grove, a manufacturer of construction cranes and heavy duty aerial ladders, introduced a new type of aerial device in 1972. Grove engineered an elevating platform basket attached to an aerial ladder, combining the best features of both into one unit. Two years later, Grove was acquired by LTI, and this design continued to be actively marketed.

To replace the large fleet of O-11 crash units serving the Air Force worldwide, a new vehicle, designated the P-4, began entering Air Force service in 1973. This new vehicle, built by Oshkosh on a six-wheel-drive chassis, carried 1,500 gallons of water and 180 gallons of foam.

A manufacturer with a different outlook on the industry began building fire apparatus in 1974. Constructing all-aluminum bodies of modular design, Emergency-One would become one of the largest fire apparatus manufacturers in the United States. The design and construction of modular alu-

minum bodywork resulted in fast delivery times unheard of in the fire apparatus industry up to this time.

During the early to mid-1970s, many fire departments began to experiment with lightweight large diameter hose carried on large reels for use as supply lines. These reels were reminiscent of the old horse-drawn hose reels, only larger. The new reels were installed on new pumpers and retrofitted to older ones. Some departments created separate hose reel or hose tender units, modern hose wagons. While still in use to some extent, the rapid deployment afforded by large diameter hose traditionally carried flat in the hose bed superseded the advantages of the hose reel.

The United States entered a recession in the mid-1970s which imposed financial hardship and caused cutbacks in many industries. City governments were especially hard hit with severe financial restrictions during this period. At the same time, production costs of new apparatus started to escalate rapidly. Funds for new apparatus were drastically cut back, especially in the major cities in the Northeast. Some large cities would not purchase any new fire apparatus for several years.

In an effort to save money and continue production of fire apparatus, Ward LaFrance and Maxim combined resources in 1976. This action only staved off the inevitable for a few years, with Ward LaFrance ceasing production in 1980. Some employees of Ward LaFrance formed a new firm, known as Ward 79 Limited, which started production in 1980. It too would last only a few years.

An ultra-large capacity airport crash vehicle was introduced into the Air Force's inventory beginning in 1978. Built by Oshkosh on an eight-wheel-drive chassis, the P-15 was developed specifically for protection of jumbo aircraft. It carries 6,100 gallons of water, 515 gallons of foam, is over 45 feet long, and is capable of driving over 18-inch-high obstructions. Designed to drive around a burning aircraft while laying down a blanket of foam, the unit is equipped with large, front and rear roof-mounted turrets. Like all Air Force firefighting vehicles, the P-15 is air-transportable.

Rebuilding fire apparatus had always been done to a small degree, and usually to apparatus that had been damaged

To replace its aging fleet of O-10 and O-11 crash units, the U.S.A.F. contracted with Oshkosh to construct the P-4. These were built on six-wheel-drive chassis and carried 1,500 gallons of water and 180 gallons of foam.

Right: A new player entered the apparatus industry in 1974 when Emergency-One started to construct modular aluminum bodies. At first Emergency-One utilized commercial chassis but soon started to introduce its own custom-built chassis.

Below: Large diameter hose carried on reels added another tool to the fire-fighting arsenal. Many older apparatus were retrofitted with these reels.

during firefighting or in vehicular accidents. However, a new sub-industry emerged in the early 1980s, partly because of many fire departments still being financially strapped and partly because of the skyrocketing costs of new apparatus. A total rebuild and overhaul of an apparatus could result in substantially extending its life span at a fraction of the cost of a new vehicle. Another major factor that hastened the growth of this industry was a decision by New York City, in 1980, to dispose of a large number of apparatus that were deemed no longer fit for use. These vehicles, usually ten to twelve years old, were basically mechanically sound but battle scarred from heavy fire duty and hundreds of thousands of responses. Many smaller departments purchased these vehicles at a bargain price and had them completely rebuilt for their own use. Other fire departments soon followed New York's lead. Many firms sprang up that were dedicated to refurbishing used fire apparatus and most of the major manufacturers followed suit, some establishing dedicated rebuilding centers. Today, refurbishing apparatus is almost as common as purchasing new ones.

At around the same time, roll-up compartment doors began to appear on American fire apparatus. These had been popular on European firefighting vehicles for quite some time.

Roll-up compartment doors offer the advantage of providing unobstructed access to compartments, especially when apparatus are positioned closely on the fireground and there is insufficient space to open a hinged compartment door. In addition, hinged compartment doors left open in the haste of fireground operations become targets for inattentive motorists. Roll-up compartment doors were installed on many refurbished apparatus and are now quite popular on new units as well.

An overall awareness of environmental hazards, coupled with highly publicized disasters involving chemicals led to a deeper, widespread involvement in these areas by the fire service beginning in the early 1980s. Specially trained and equipped teams were formed to mitigate the release of and minimize the damage from hazardous materials spills and incidents. Much specialized equipment and chemical protective suits were developed especially for this function. Along with the teams and equipment came dedicated apparatus to

carry them. At first, fire departments tried to add this equipment to regular apparatus, but as the volume and variety of equipment grew, the need for dedicated haz-mat apparatus was established. Initially, these covered a wide range, including converted delivery vans, pumpers, mobile homes, mechanics' trucks, rescue trucks, and even trailers towed by other vehicles. Eventually haz-mat units would evolve into vehicles similar in size and design to heavy rescue trucks. Many would incorporate command post areas. Quite a few fire departments opted to utilize vehicles similar in design to beverage delivery trucks while still others use tractor trailers.

Several amphibious firefighting vehicles were constructed during the 1980s in an attempt to provide fireboat capabilities coupled with the advantages of housing such units in existing fire stations, staffing them with existing personnel that were cross trained to operated them, and providing greater operational flexibility. Firefighting equipment was

To meet the hazards of jumbo jets, the largest crash rescue vehicle built to date began joining the U.S.A.F. roster in 1978. The P-15 is over 45 feet long, carries 6,100 gallons of water, 515 gallons of foam, and was built by Oshkosh on an eight-wheel-drive chassis that can drive over 18-inch-high obstructions.

Rebuilding fire apparatus came of age during the 1980s. Left: A former New York City 1980 American LaFrance in service at a local volunteer department. Below: Bearing little resemblance to its original appearance while serving New York, this 1978 Mack CF Aerialscope has been remounted on a 1994 FWD chassis for Kentland, MD.

mounted on bulky military style LARC vehicles that had large, oversize tires for use on land. Miami, Tampa, and Milwaukee all purchased and operated such vehicles. Unfortunately, they proved to be extremely maintenance intensive, and were slow when traveling on land.

Ever-increasing concern for firefighter safety led to the introduction of larger, enclosed cabs capable of accommodating more firefighters inside. In 1984, Spartan introduced their "Super Command" cab built on a Gladiator chassis. This cab has seating for ten firefighters and has full stand-up height in its rear portion. Also in 1984, Mack Trucks announced that they would no longer construct complete fire apparatus; however, their fire chassis would continue to be produced and be available to other manufacturers.

Increasing demand for medical services provided by fire departments sometimes overtaxed available resources. In

Pawtucket, RI, had this 1967 Maxim 100-foot tiller rebuilt and repowered by a 1987 Hahn tractor, extending its useful life span by quite a few years.

Concurrent with the coming of age of apparatus rebuilding, roll-up compartment doors began to appear on American built and refurbished apparatus. Milwaukee operated this 1985 LTI tiller, pulled by a Ford tractor, and equipped with roll-up compartment doors.

The awareness of chemical and environmental hazards led to the establishment of separate haz-mat units. Los Angeles City operated units built by Saulsbury on 1992 Seagrave chassis.

some areas, ambulances were sometimes all assigned to incidents, and EMTs and paramedics who responded on pumpers would be forced to wait at the scene with victims until an ambulance became available. A handful of innovative departments attempted to rectify this situation by designing a pumper that incorporated an ambulance module which enabled the victim to be transported by the pumper when ambulances were unavailable. The first of this type of unit entered service during 1985. A more popular design, gaining widespread acceptance, was the standard pumper with additional compartmentation dedicated to carrying EMS equipment, but not capable of transporting victims. Many fire

departments staffed such units with paramedics, providing both structural firefighting and advanced life support services. These paramedic engines became popular in areas where the majority of the department's responses were to medical emergencies, providing both services at the reduced cost of only one crew.

During the same year American LaFrance operations in Elmira, New York, ceased. Limited production was undertaken in Bluefield, Virginia. The 1980s and 1990s were a period of upheaval in the fire apparatus industry. Many long-time manufacturers reorganized or completely shut down their operations. Other, smaller manufacturers came into existence as spin-offs of these closures, often with employees of the original firms. Other manufacturers strengthened their place in the market. Acquisitions and mergers took place at an unprecedented rate for such a small industry. Changing market conditions, continued fiscal restraints on cities, the explosion of rebuilt apparatus, and increasing production costs all took their toll.

Continuing financial restrictions, not only to purchase apparatus but also in day-to-day operating budgets, forced many large fire departments to purchase quints. Unfortunately, these were usually utilized to combine engine and ladder companies into one unit and reduce manpower. This trend towards quints started around 1985 and has continued, despite the limitations of this apparatus.

One of the most unusual and innovative apparatus ever produced was introduced in 1985 by Emergency-One as their Hush chassis. This chassis has its engine mounted at the rear, remote from the cab. This design provides a quieter cab environment, better weight distribution, and allows for more firefighters to be carried in the cab.

New York City operates a two-piece haz-mat unit. This unit, which was built by Saulsbury on a 1989 Mack chassis, serves as the primary response vehicle, equipped with a command post, computer, reference library, and carrying chemical protective suits and mitigation equipment.

Right: Some fire departments, like Boca Raton, FL, utilize large tractor-trailer vehicles as their hazardous materials unit. This particular unit also carries heavy rescue equipment, extra air cylinders, lighting equipment, and serves as a command post. It was built by Southern Coach and uses an International tractor.

Left: Other fire departments opt to use vehicles similar to beverage delivery trucks as their haz-mat units. Boston's Special Hazards Response Unit operates with this 1979 Ford/Hesse that was rebuilt in 1987 by Resco.

Van Pelt Fire Truck Company, based in California, after building almost 3,200 firefighting vehicles, produced their last fire apparatus in 1987.

Awareness of the need to have specialized rescue equipment and trained personnel available to deal with building collapses, earthquakes, damage caused by severe storms and terrorist acts was brought to the forefront during the late 1980s by several major natural disasters. Many fire departments organized or expanded their heavy rescue capability in the next few years. "Urban search and rescue" became a popular term in the fire service to describe functions that heavy rescue companies in major cities had been performing for

decades. Heavy rescue trucks and support vehicles were constructed at an unprecedented rate. Some fire departments converted existing vehicles into such units. Others procured tractor trailers and roll-off containerized modules for these purposes. As an off-shoot to these heavy rescue units, even more specialized teams were created for very specific situations. SCUBA, water rescue, cave-in, collapse, high-angle rescue, cliff rescue, confined space rescue, and other highly specialized teams were formed, using apparatus specific to their purposes.

Bronto Skylift, a European elevating boom manufacturer, made its first delivery to the United States during 1990.

A small number of amphibious firefighting vehicles were built during the 1980s. Milwaukee operated this 1984 model outfitted by LTI and capable of pumping 2,500 gpm. They were slow when responding on land and required extensive maintenance after use in water.

These booms differed from those manufactured in America by being three-section articulated models and were available in greater height. Bronto Skylift would eventually be acquired by Emergency-One.

After constructing fire apparatus since the horse-drawn era, Maxim closed the doors to its assembly plant in 1990. Its equipment, tools and supplies were auctioned off along with uncompleted cabs, many of which were purchased by KME. Pirsch, another long-time apparatus manufacturer, disappeared from the scene that year as well. Sanford, who built their first fire apparatus in 1925, also ceased production during 1990. The same year, Mack Trucks announced that it would no longer build custom fire chassis, including the popular CF model.

The National Fire Protection Association, an organization devoted to all aspects of firefighting and fire protection, issued revised standards for fire apparatus during 1991. These standards would have a large impact on fire apparatus design. The revised standards called for enclosed, seated positions equipped with seat belts for all firefighters riding on the apparatus. While the fire service had been moving towards fully

Above: Modern fire apparatus have an array of different warning devices that includes side-mounted roof light bars, a center-mounted locomotive-style light, an air horn and an electronic siren mounted in the bumper to better project sound at motorists. Multi-colored reflective striping and two-tone paint add to the visibility of the vehicle.

Right: Spartan Motors introduced their Super Command Cab in 1984. Phoenix operated several of these 1985 models with Van Pelt bodywork. This cab provided more room to carry firefighters and could be used as a command post.

enclosed crew cab apparatus for some time, these standards solidified this movement. For safety reasons, it is much more desirable to have everyone on the vehicle in a seated, belted position inside the cab. Riding on the back step and other outside locations on the apparatus, along with the associated hazards of this, was deemed no longer acceptable. Other changes in the standards included two-tone color schemes and a wide reflective stripe on the apparatus. The N.F.P.A. wisely chose to refrain from specifying a color for apparatus, instead stating that a two-tone color scheme with reflective stripe made the apparatus more visible.

Coupled with the N.F.P.A. standards, several federal laws and mandates also affected the construction of fire apparatus. Engine size, vehicle emissions, axle loading, introduction of anti-lock brake systems, and others have all added to the cost of fire apparatus production, helping to triple the cost of custom-built vehicles over the last two decades, and contributing to greater use of commercial chassis for apparatus construction.

The depressed state of the nation's economy continued to have a devastating effect on an industry in upheaval. Within the next two years Beck, Crown, Grumman, Hahn, and Ward 79 would all cease production of fire apparatus.

With every advance in firefighting comes resulting, often unforeseen, problems. Widespread use of bunker gear, fire clothing that consists of bulky protective pants and coats, along with protective hoods, resulted in firefighters that were virtually encapsulated. The use of this gear, while a distinct safety advantage, especially in protecting against burn injuries, also rapidly depletes the firefighters' ability to work and accelerates dehydration, especially in hot, humid weather. Fireground rehabilitation units help to alleviate this situation. These vehicles are large, air conditioned units, providing a

Many fire departments, suffering from budget constraints, attempted to use quints in place of engine and ladder companies, to get the most out of scarce dollars. St. Louis became the largest user of this type of apparatus, assigning one to every engine company, and closing most ladder companies. The success of this type of unit is limited and based on many factors including building construction, response area congestion, manpower and tactics.

With the introduction of the Hush chassis by Emergency-One, firefighters were afforded a more quiet environment inside the cab. The interior noise level was greatly reduced and better overall weight distribution was achieved by mounting the engine at the rear.

rest area removed from weather extremes, where firefighters can be examined by medical personnel and be afforded the opportunity to rest and recuperate for a period of time prior to returning to work. These vehicles often carry refrigerated liquids and are sometimes equipped with water misting equipment to accelerate the rehab time. Converted heavy rescue trucks, bus-type vehicles, and recreation vehicles have been commonly used for this purpose.

In an effort to combat fires in large frame, wide body, jumbo aircraft, particularly fires in the tail-mounted engine, several manufacturers attempted to design elevating boom devices for mounting on airport fire apparatus. Crash Rescue

Equipment Service constructed a 50-foot articulated/telescopic boom, known as the Snozzle, which is capable of supplying water or foam to elevated portions of aircraft. Other equipment, including piercing nozzles, capable of piercing the aircraft's skin, floodlights, and video cameras for inspection of hard to see areas of the aircraft, could be mounted on the boom. The Snozzle became quite popular, and was mounted on many newly built airport apparatus, retrofitted to older units, and even mounted on several structural units.

Both S&S Fire Apparatus, using a Spartan chassis, and Pierce started marketing a rear-wheel steering option on their apparatus in 1994. It is interesting to note that when this inno-

Right: Built on a Mercedes-Benz chassis, this German pumper typifies the standardization of European fire apparatus, with enclosed crew cab, roll-up compartment doors, and all equipment carried inside.

Left: This large capacity airport crash rescue vehicle was built by Reynolds Boughton for Heathrow Airport in England.

New York City has always maintained well-equipped heavy rescue units to deal with building collapses and other technical rescue situations. Widespread natural disasters nationwide was the catalyst for many fire departments to form similar urban search and rescue teams.

Large van-style trucks are needed to carry the amount of equipment required by a heavy rescue unit. Saulsbury built this heavy rescue truck on a 1985 Mack chassis.

vation was introduced by Seagrave on its Rear Admiral aerials it wasn't very popular, yet almost thirty years later, it again surfaced. In those thirty years, apparatus have greatly increased in size and weight, and so has traffic congestion, even in suburban areas. Perhaps rear steering will become more popular the second time around.

Many fire departments have been faced with dwindling staffing. Mandated training requirements, commuting long distances to work, lack of available time, and other factors, all impose hardships on volunteer departments while financially strapped paid departments are constantly struggling to maintain adequate staffing. Fire departments have developed multi-function vehicles to maximize the use of this limited personnel, providing several functions with one vehicle. These units are usually larger and bulkier and are generally built on three-axle chassis. An added advantage is a financial savings in purchasing separate vehicles. Combinations such as

pumper-tankers, rescue-pumpers, and haz-mat pumpers are becoming popular in rural and suburban areas, while foam pumpers, EMS pumpers and paramedic engines are more common in urban areas.

An unusual combination apparatus, the ladder-tender, is becoming very popular with fire departments where the majority of responses are non-fire and medical emergencies. The ladder tender is assigned as the second apparatus of a ladder company and carries the same equipment as the ladder truck does except for ladders. It also carries a complete complement of EMS equipment. When a non-fire response is received, the ladder company responds in the ladder tender, leaving the ladder truck in the station. While away from the station in the ladder tender, the unit still has the capabilities to respond to fires and perform all ladder company functions except for laddering. This is an efficient use of manpower while saving wear and tear on the expensive ladder trucks.

Above left: The amount of new rescue equipment being introduced into the fire service for unusual rescue operations often outgrows available space on heavy-rescue apparatus. New York operates tactical support units that carry small boats, water rescue equipment, a generator and portable lighting equipment, an air compressor, and a full complement of hydraulic tools.

Collapse rescue, also termed urban search and rescue, has evolved into a highly specialized field, complete with equipment specifically developed for this purpose. This specialized collapse rescue vehicle was built by SuperVac and is pulled by a 1995 Ford tractor.

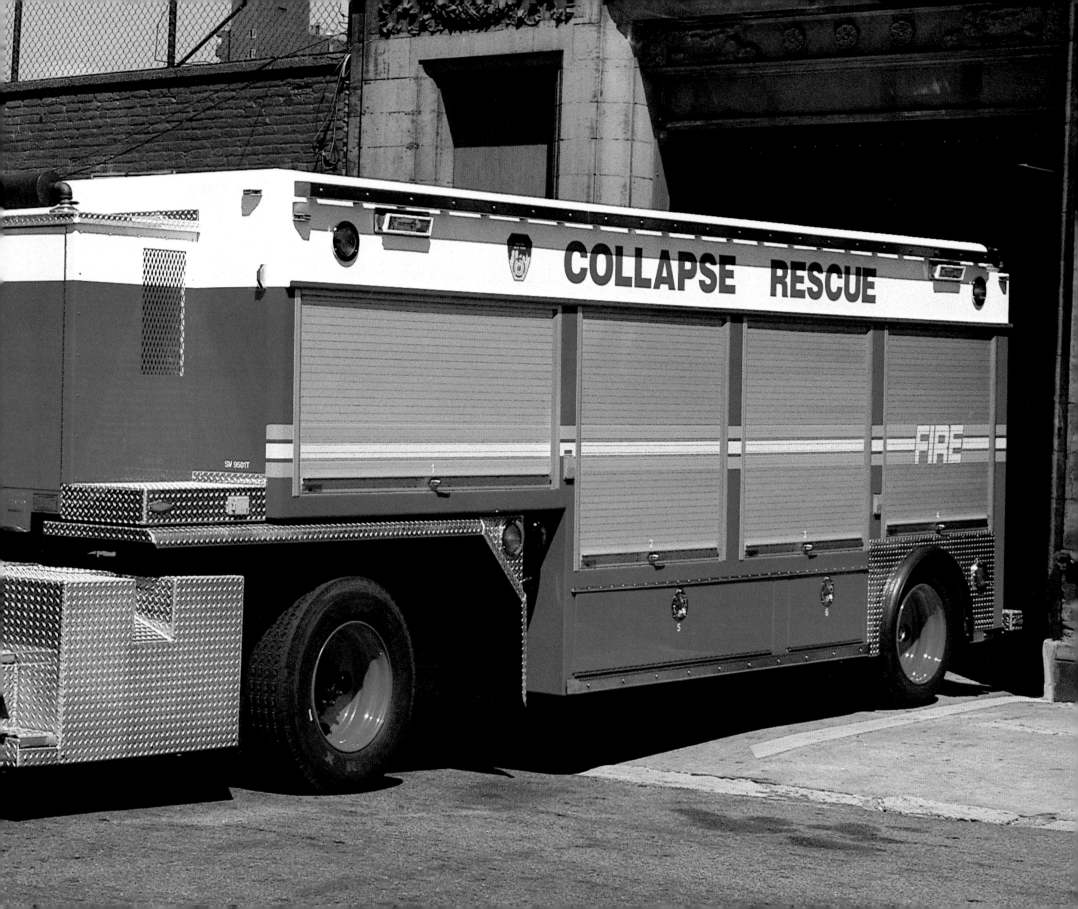

Roll-off containerized units, very popular in Europe, offer the advantage of using one chassis with any number of containers, each having its own purpose. Montgomery County, MD, operates this 1988 Mack carrying a container set up for cave-in and trench rescue operations.

What will we see on future fire apparatus? The trend towards apparatus being built by specialized body builders on commercially available chassis will continue, as will refurbishing and rebuilding existing apparatus. More American fire apparatus will be built on foreign chassis even though only a small number are so built today. Fire apparatus will also take on a more standard, European, look with more being built with roll-up compartment doors. Automation and technology will be incorporated to a larger degree to maximize the use of personnel and provide a safer environment. Alternate fuel powered fire apparatus are sure to come, but like any change, will be slow to take hold. Apparatus will continue to grow in size but more specialized units will be built to perform dedicated functions. And most importantly, fire trucks will certainly continue to be interesting, eye-catching vehicles!

Many specialized rescue situations require trained teams and specific equipment. Among the more common are water rescue situations, and many fire departments operate SCUBA units. Monroe, NY, uses this GMC delivery van for its underwater search and recovery unit.

Above: A European manufacturer, Bronto Skylift, offers its elevating plat-form in various heights to be mounted on American built chassis. This 103-foot boom is mounted on a 1991 Pemfab chassis and is in service in Mineola, NY.

Right: Older fire apparatus carried almost all equipment on the running boards or mounted on the sides, exposed and ready for immediate use. Modern vehicles carry all equipment inside compartments, often locked to protect the equipment from theft.

*Fireground rehabilitation has become
more important with the introduction
of bunker equipment for firefighters.
Phoenix, AZ, converted this former rescue truck, a 1978 Mack with
Gerstenslager bodywork, into a rehabilitation unit.*

*The Snozzle boom was developed by
Crash Rescue Equipment Service to
combat fires in large wide-body aircraft. This 50-foot Snozzle is mounted
on a 1994 Oshkosh serving Phoenix.*

As contemporary apparatus continue to grow in size, rear steering options are beginning to appear on more vehicles. This option offers greater maneuverability, especially in very congested traffic or tight street conditions. Council Bluffs, IA, operates this 1995 Pierce equipped with the All Wheel Steer option.

The U.S. Military Academy at West Point operates this rescue-pumper as Engine 4. It is a 1995 Emergency-One 1,250 gpm pumper, equipped with a 500-gallon tank, front-mounted winch, full-height compartments for rescue equipment, and a hydraulic rescue tool system. It provides both pumper and rescue services at a housing area remote from the main base.

The ever-increasing demand for emergency medical services has resulted in many fire departments staffing and equipping engine companies with firefighters who are also paramedics. Paramedic Engine 18 in Phoenix operates with this Emergency-One Hush pumper.

In areas that are remote from water supply, the fire department must bring its own water to the fire. This pumper-tanker in Fairfax County, VA, carries 2,000 gallons of water and is equipped with a 1,250 gpm pump. This unit was built by American Eagle on a Freightliner chassis.

Ladder tenders are providing fire departments that respond to numerous EMS responses with a practical alternative to responding to medical emergencies with larger, more expensive ladder trucks. These units carry all ladder company equipment except for ladders and also carry a full complement of EMS equipment. This unit was built by Emergency-One on an International chassis.

Commercial chassis with crew cabs are becoming more common in today's modern fire service and are gaining a large share of the market when compared to custom-built chassis. Darley built the bodywork on this International chassis for San Juan, Puerto Rico.

Although still in small numbers, more foreign-built chassis are being used for fire apparatus in America than ever before. North Fort Myers, FL, operates this Mercedes-Benz with Quality bodywork.

Following the cessation of production of the Mack CF chassis which Baker used exclusively to mount their Aerialscope on, several optional chassis were used for this boom. This is a 1994 FWD chassis with Saulsbury bodywork and a 75-foot Baker Aerialscope boom.

PHOTO CREDITS

All photos are by the author except for the following: Bob Allen: 64 top; Eugene Anderson: 97; Charles Beckwith: 4, 33 top; Eugene Belle: 26; Leo Duliba: 125; FAJ Collection: 7, 8 top, 9, 10 bottom, 11 bottom, 12 top, 13 top, 14 top, 16 bottom, 18, 22 top, 37; FAJ Collection/FJR: 2, 11 top, 32; Manfred Gihl: 69 bottom, 107 top; Dave Greenberg: 118, 123; A. Henry: 43, 107 bottom; Ron Jeffers: 94 top; Pete Lund: 116 top; Dennis Maag: 24-25, 105, 119; Charles Madderom: 52, 98-99, 100, 103; Bob Milnes: 102 top; Elena Miranda: 5, 6, 14 bottom, 19 bottom, 21 top, 22 bottom, 23 top, 24 top, 30 bottom, 36 bottom, 42 top, 84 top, 88 bottom, 116 bottom; William Noonan: 102 bottom; William Noonan Collection: 8 bottom, 10 top, 12 bottom, 15, 16 top; Joe Pinto: 79 top; Mark A. Redman: 86 top; James Regan: 59; Steve Schueler: 88 bottom; Shaun Ryan: 42 bottom, 106, 124; Tom Shand: 96 bottom, 104 bottom, 117, 121; John A. Toomey: 39, 72-73, 74; Glenn Vincent: 77 bottom; Joel Woods: 13 bottom, 17, 31, 35, 70, 78 bottom, 88 top, 114, 122.